Level 1

Re-told by: Nicola Schofield
Series Editor: Rachel Wilson

Before You Read

In This Book

Peter Pan

Tinker Bell

John
Wendy
Michael

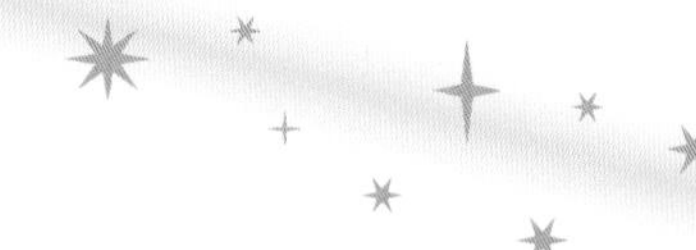

Activity

Read and say.

1 Peter Pan is …
- **a** an animal
- **b** a boy
- **c** a baby

2 Michael is …
- **a** a bird
- **b** a boy
- **c** a flower

3 London is …
- **a** a city
- **b** a house
- **c** an animal

This is the city of London. Who lives here?

Wendy, John, and Michael live in London.

They live in a big house. They are in bed.

Peter Pan and Tinker Bell are in London.

They come to the big house. They go in.

Peter Pan and Tinker Bell fly in the bedroom.

Peter Pan likes this house.
The bedroom is big.

John, Wendy, and young Michael see a boy.

It's Peter Pan ... and Tinker Bell.
They live in Never Land.

Never Land is magical.

Peter Pan, Tinker Bell, and the children fly to Never Land.

Peter Pan, Tinker Bell,
and the children fly and fly.

They see Big Ben. They are happy.
Bye bye, London!

Hello, Never Land!
It is beautiful.

After You Read

1 Complete the sentences. Choose words from the box.

children London magical Never Land fly

1 Wendy, John, and Michael are from ....
2 The .... live in a big house.
3 Peter Pan and Tinker Bell are from ....
4 Peter Pan and Tinker Bell .... in the bedroom.
5 Never Land is ....

2 Read and say Yes or No.

1 There are two children.
2 Peter Pan has a blue hat.
3 The children are happy.
4 They fly to Peter Land.

Picture Dictionary

fly

happy

house

magical

Phonics

Say the sounds. Read the words.

B b

P p

Say the tongue twister.

In the big bedroom,
Peter Pan plays.

Values

Try something new.

Find Out

What is a monument?

Monuments are important buildings.
Big Ben is a monument in London.
Now look at these monuments.

Chichen Itza in Mexico
FACT: It's an old city.

The Eiffel Tower in Paris
FACT: There are two restaurants.

The Burj Khalifa in Dubai
FACT: It's tall.

The Taj Mahal in India
FACT: There are beautiful gardens.

Pearson Education Limited
KAO Two
KAO Park, Harlow,
Essex, CM17 9NA, England
and Associated Companies throughout the world.

ISBN: 978-1-2923-4665-6

This edition first published by Pearson Education Ltd 2020

1 3 5 7 9 10 8 6 4 2

Set in Heinemann Roman Special, 19pt/28pt
Printed by Neografia, Slovakia

Published by Pearson Education Limited

Acknowledgments
Getty Images: ilbusca 16, JekaterinaVassilenko 18, PytyCzech 21, Steven dosRemedios 20
Shutterstock.com: DrAndY 20-21, Paul Wishart 17, S-F 21, turtix 21, Vastram 18, WDG Photo 20

For a complete list of the titles available in the Pearson English Readers series, visit www.pearsonenglishreaders.com.

Alternatively, write to your local Pearson Education office or to Pearson English Readers Marketing Department, Pearson Education, KAO Two, KAO Park, Harlow, Essex, CM17 9NA